bang

in the wild

groovy chick's diaries

keep out

Yay!

First day of summer hol.

Things to do:

Major lie-in

Get to know my duvet

Cuddle up with dog

Play groovy music

Read fab mags

Watch TV

Laze about

Walk the dog

4

Great goss with my mates.
We are going to summer
camp on Wednesday.

Can't wait!

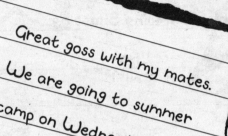

Only one sad
is the dog.

Tuesday am

Camping Shopping List

Sweets

Moisturiser

Sun cream

Insect repellent

Sting cream

Fake tan

Bickies

6

Summer camp tomorrow!

Farewell dinner with Mum 'n' Dad.

Yummy spaghetti.

Early night after

good long soak

in bubbly

bath.

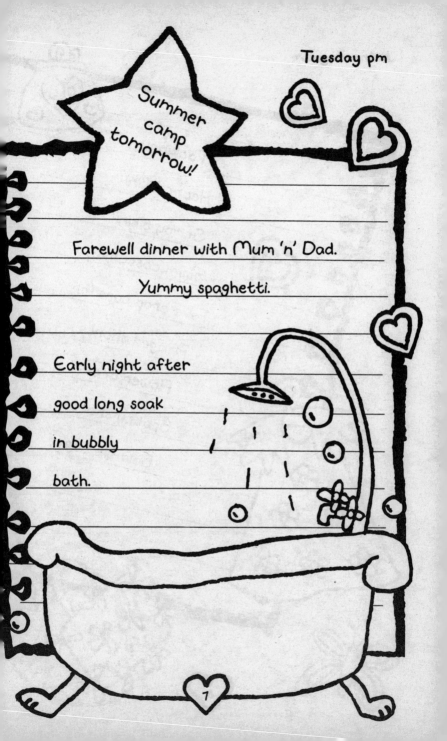

Packing:

Heart bikini

Stripy bikini

Swim costume

Fave crop tops (6)

Fringed shorts

Flower dress

Spotty shorts

Bow tie bag

8

2 pairs of jeans (one glam for discos!)

Gypsy top and skirt

Denim jacket

Flip-flops

Party sandals

Sparkly purse

Scrummy packed lunch

for coach ride!

~~Fave cuddly toy~~ – too babyish

Set up camp yesterday!

It was well funny.

Tent collapsed in a heap on top of us a

zillion times. Got fit of the giggles!

Ha! Ha!

Hee! Hee!

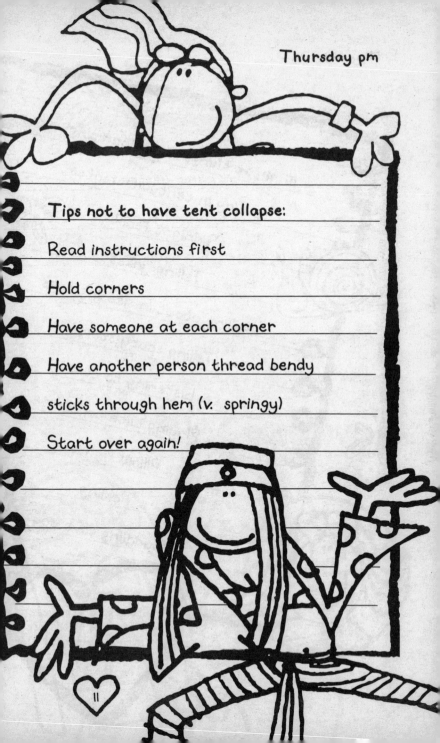

Tips not to have tent collapse:

Read instructions first

Hold corners

Have someone at each corner

Have another person thread bendy

sticks through hem (v. springy)

Start over again!

11

10 great things about camping:

Sleeping in tent with mates

Midnight feasts

Telling jokes

Rolling about in sleeping bags

Telling scary stories

Listening to owls

Playing with torches

Pillow fights

Tickling

Cuddling fave toy

(Thank goodness I ran back for mine at the last minute. Everybody else brought theirs!)

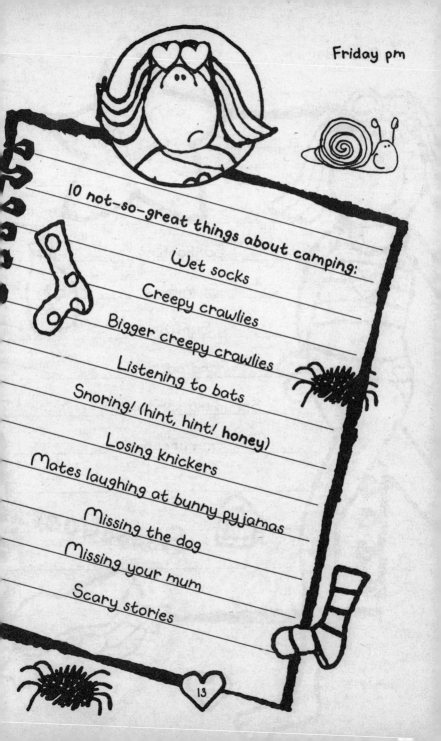

10 not-so-great things about camping:

Wet socks

Creepy crawlies

Bigger creepy crawlies

Listening to bats

Snoring! (hint, hint! honey)

Losing knickers

Mates laughing at bunny pyjamas

Missing the dog

Missing your mum

Scary stories

Saturday am

Time for beach!

Sunbathing

Swimming

Surfing

Sand castles

Scrummy sandwiches

Sun cream

Ssssuper!

14

Got fish 'n' chips for tea. Sat on wall

and ate them while tide went out.

Mmmmmm!

Isn't summertime the **best**?

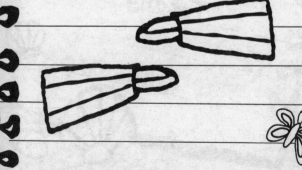

We decided to decorate tent with a seaside theme. Used things we found on beach and in cool local shops. Lots of groovy ideas!

Streamers

Shells on string

Sparkly windmills

Totally wicked!

Cool sing-song round camp-fire:

There was **pop princess**,
Princess, princess.
Getting in a mess.
In the tent,
In the tent!

There was **happy girl**,
Girl, girl.
Getting in a whirl.
In the tent,
In the tent!

Night, night!

Week

Two

Hiking today!

5 good things about hiking are:

Fresh air

Exercise

Picking wildflowers

Finding things

Wildlife

20

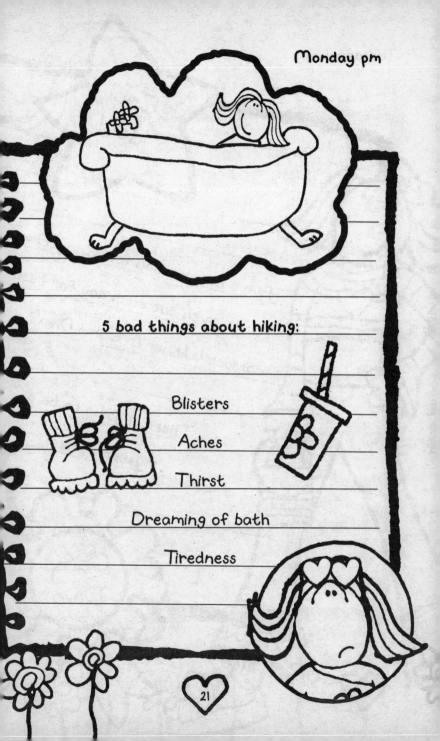

5 bad things about hiking:

Blisters

Aches

Thirst

Dreaming of bath

Tiredness

Cool idea!

Have a competition for "Camp Diva".

Points given out each day for best

camper. Winner is "Camp Diva"!

There is going to be a

mystery prize!

Camp Diva

22

2 points

COOK OUT

Sausages

Baked beans (whoops!)

Baked potatoes

Scrummy
Yummy

2 points to surf babe

for not burning

sausages.

23

Queue for camp shower gets longer everyday. (I'm counting!)

Beauty tips for campers:

Stick jewels on toenails

Wear rings on toes

Sparkly flip-flops are tops

(if no cow pats around!)

Wear socks in sleeping bag

(otherwise you lose them)

Major cool game of football on

campsite.

Lost to the red team!

Boo hoo!

Camp
is fun!

Totally groovy beach party today.

Picnic, music,

dancing.

Yay!

I won 5 points as

best rock chick!

Yessssss!

Will I be Camp Diva?

Dancing on the sand totally rocks.
We danced to all sorts of tunes –
rock, disco, hip-hop and pop!

5
points

27

Fetching water duty.

It's official! Water weighs a ton!

Here's my postcard to Mum 'n' Dad.

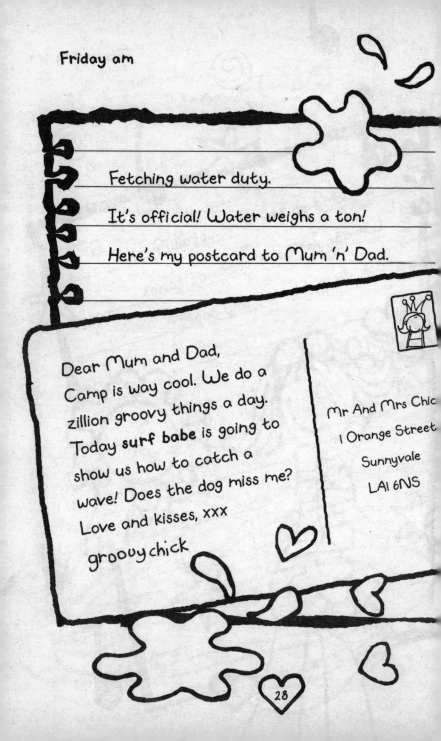

Dear Mum and Dad,
Camp is way cool. We do a
zillion groovy things a day.
Today **surf babe** is going to
show us how to catch a
wave! Does the dog miss me?
Love and kisses, xxx

groovy chick

Mr And Mrs Chic
1 Orange Street
Sunnyvale
LA1 6NS

5 points

Surfing is mega cool, surf babe got 5 points today. She is a top surfer!

Saturday am

Spent a very cloudy day at beach.

Had a competition to see who could

collect the prettiest shells.

Pop princess won, she got 5 Camp

Diva points.

5 points

30

We all made things with shell collection. I decorated a box for my mum. V. pretty!

Quiet day (except for funky girl's jokes).

Here's one...

Q. What do you use to paint a rabbit?

A. Hare spray!

31

We learned about snorkelling today.

Was a bit hard to do the breathing.

But once we got it sorted, was totally

groovy. I saw tons of fish (and lots of

seaweed)!

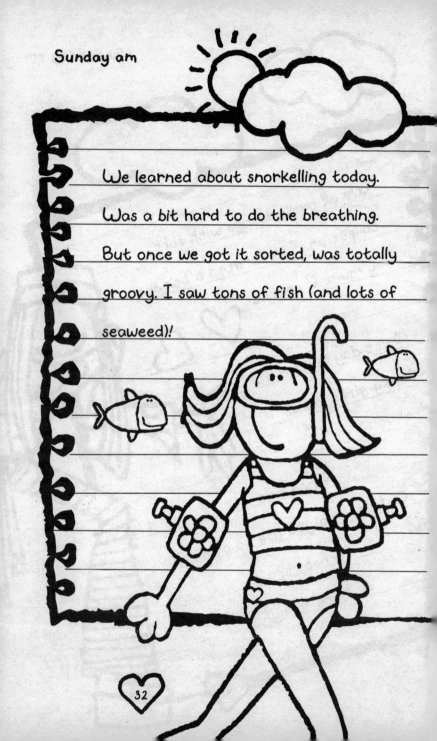

5
Points

Won 5 points as

best diver! Yesss!

I miss my dog!
I miss my dog!

Playing with computer games under

our sleeping bags is the latest

craze.......G'night!

33

Egg 'n' bacon for breakfast. Yummy.

Sandcastle competition today. V. hot, covered myself in sun cream.

Decided to build sandcastles with a bucket and spade we found on beach. Here is a picture of my castle.

I won second place, 10 points towards Camp Diva comp!

10 points

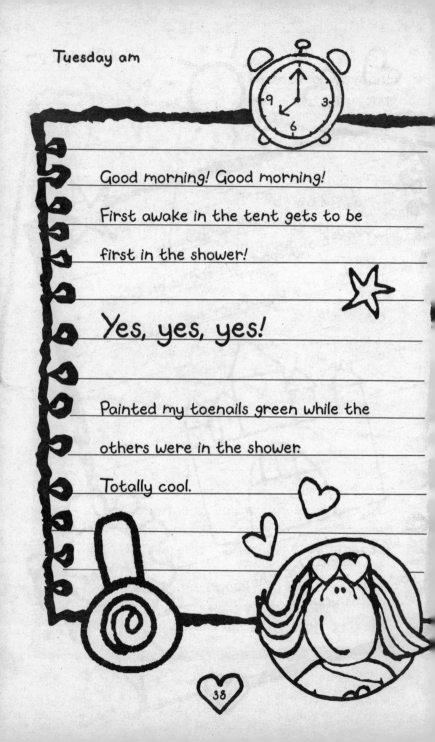

Good morning! Good morning!

First awake in the tent gets to be

first in the shower!

Yes, yes, yes!

Painted my toenails green while the

others were in the shower.

Totally cool.

Another postcard to
groovy mum!

Dear Mum,
Please, please can you send
me my red glitter top and
blue shimmer nail polish? We
are having a disco on
Saturday and I want
to be your groovy
chick. Luv U Mum

groovy chick xxxx

Mr And Mrs Chick
1 Orange Street
Sunnyvale
LA1 6NS

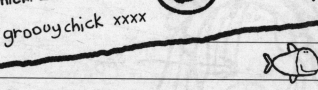

Swimming and fishing in rock pools.

Just in time for an ice cream before

heading back to camp.

Ice cream after swimming in the sea

is extra delicious!

Honey is more glum than glam.
She has a big spot on her nose
(totally un-glam), and no spot
remedies.

Eeeww!

spot

Stray cat came to visit our tent. That cheered up honey!

We got a saucer of milk from the camp kitchen.

41

Thursday am

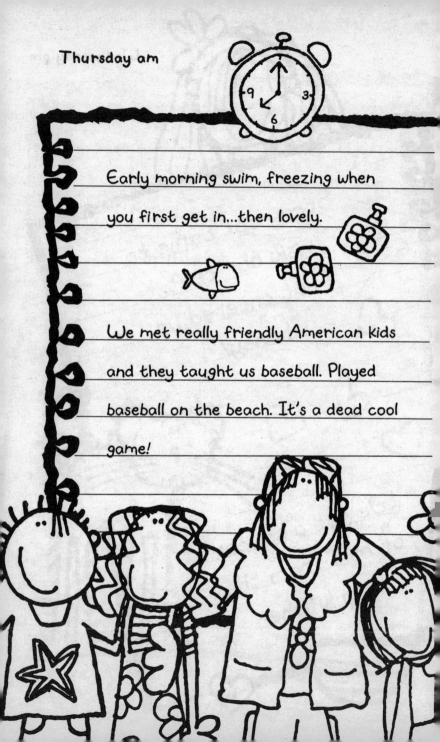

Early morning swim, freezing when you first get in...then lovely.

We met really friendly American kids and they taught us baseball. Played baseball on the beach. It's a dead cool game!

Read fab mags.

Must remember to follow fashion advice.

Did Star Quality quiz.

I have the most

star quality!

From groovy mum!

Dear groovy chick,
Here is the gear you asked
me to send. Have fun
wearing it at the disco. We
all miss you. Be careful
swimming. Watch out for
the sharks!
Love Mum
xxx

groovy chick

Camp Sunshine

Devon

We made up our own
Disco Diva quiz!

Are you a Disco Diva?

Your idea of a cool disco drink is:

a) A glass of milk?

b) An ice cold cola?

c) A fizzy fruit cocktail?

The music blasts out. Do you:

a) Cover your ears?

b) Munch on nibbles?

c) Show off those poptastic moves?

Your hair is a mess. Do you:

a) Leave it?

b) Fuss until you're late?

c) Pin it with groovy clips?

Your mum thinks you are too young to wear make-up. Do you:

a) Go to disco with scrubbed face?

b) Put make-up on in disco loos?

c) Show your mum how shimmery gel can make eyes, lips and cheeks groovy?

Your best friend is shy. Do you:

a) Leave her in the corner?

b) Tell her to get a life?

c) Teach her poptastic dance moves?

You have nothing to wear to the disco? Do you:

a) Wear school uniform?

b) Borrow your mum's party gear?

c) Jazz up old jeans with glitter?

Conclusions

Mostly A – Sleepy Sista!

Mostly B – Party Person!

Mostly C – Disco Diva!

We spent all day getting ready for the camp disco.

There were clothes and make-up all over the tent!

Funky girl got 5 points for being the first to get ready and she looked great.

5 points

Disco night!

Disco was totally fab!

We danced all night, and

everybody looked very groovy.

Camp leader said he was glad

we were all enjoying ourselves

so much.

We all want to come

back next year!

Sunday am

Lazed around all day.
Made each other up.
Tried out hairstyles
from mags.

Hanging out with
friends is so cool!

We made up another cool camp song...

There was **groovy chick**,
Chick, chick.
Playing a groovy trick,
In the tent,
In the tent!

There was **funky girl**,
Girl, girl.
Doing a funky twirl.
In the tent,
In the tent.

Night , night!

Went for a walk by the sea. Picked flowers and made flower necklaces. V. pretty.

Dreamed of dog and my bed at

home. Miss my pet!

Beach then lunch.
I was so hungry I
ate loads!

Carried a pretty
tote bag with
all my stuff.

This is my funky beach to camp look. I jazz up my hair with fancy clips and add some groovy flip-flops. I got 5 points for being the best dressed on the beach.

5 points

55

Wednesday am

Yum!

My fave foods at camp are:

French Fries
Hot Dogs
Cola
Fruity Munchies

56

Yum!

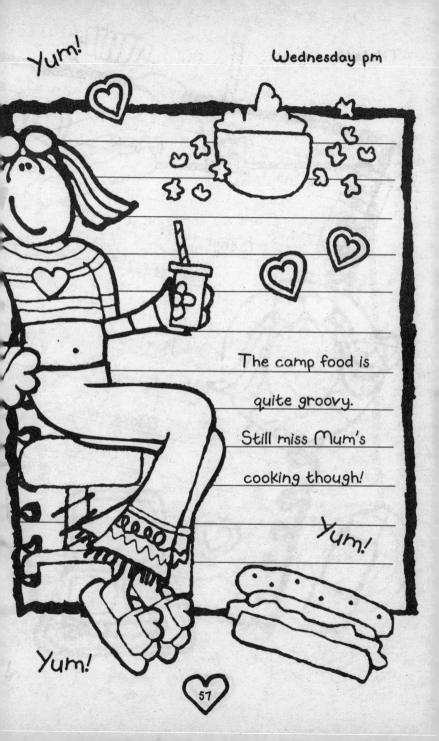

Yum!

The camp food is

quite groovy.

Still miss Mum's

cooking though!

Yum!

Yum!

Oh, no! Lost my fave lip gloss.

Other stuff lost by me and my mates:

Hairbrush

Watch

Make-up

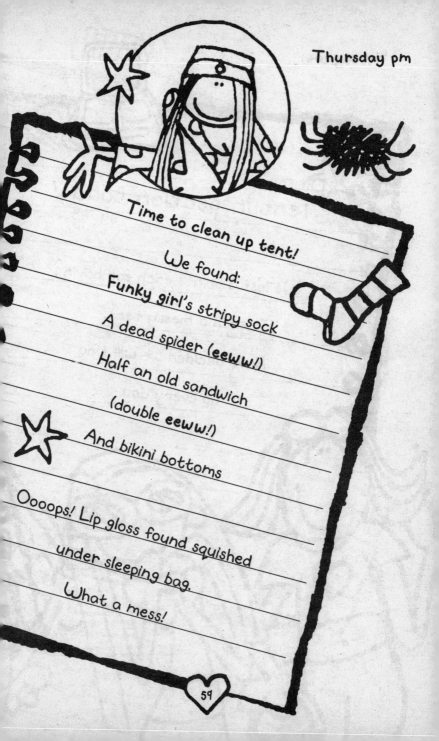

Time to clean up tent!

We found:

Funky girl's stripy sock

A dead spider (**eeww!**)

Half an old sandwich

(double **eeww!**)

And bikini bottoms

Oooops! Lip gloss found squished

under sleeping bag.

What a mess!

Friday am

★ Tent inspection today!

We lost 5 points each for having

such a messy tent.

Have decided we will tidy

up every day.

We have done
no tidying!
Too busy lying
around in the sunshine.

We love

camp!

Saturday am

Meeting American friends from other day.

Fave meeting spots:

Boating pond

Ice cream van

Wall on the seafront

Chippy

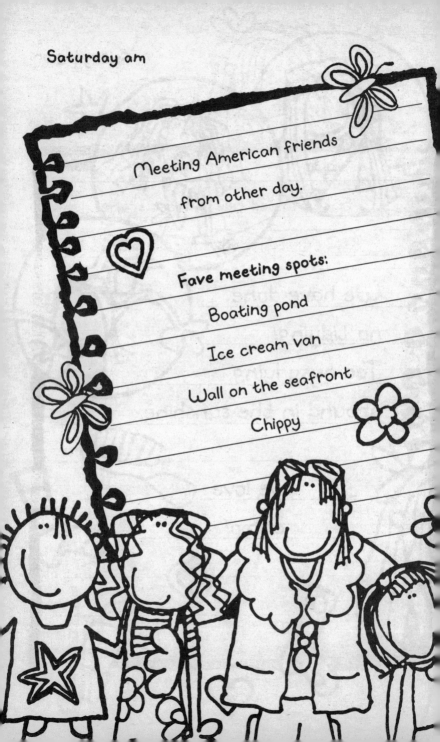

Sat up in bed telling ghost stories.

Really creepy. **Honey** totally freaked

out and hid in her sleeping bag.

I had to go to the loo in the dark.

Eeeek!

Rustling in the bushes! Nearly didn't

make it! Major cringe! Rustling in

bushes was not a ghost.

It was the cat.

Pheew!

Our most embarrassing moments

Coming out of toilets with skirt tucked into pants! Shame!

Falling SPLAT into a cowpat Yuck!

Snoring like a tractor in tent all night! ZZzzz

Being the only one at the party in fancy dress!

Saying 'thank you' when gift is for someone else.

Wearing clothes inside out by mistake.

Oh, no!

Sitting on your lipstick and getting lipstick on your pants!

Leaving a glob of moisturiser under your nose.

Snotty, or what?

Ripping your bikini!

Oooops!

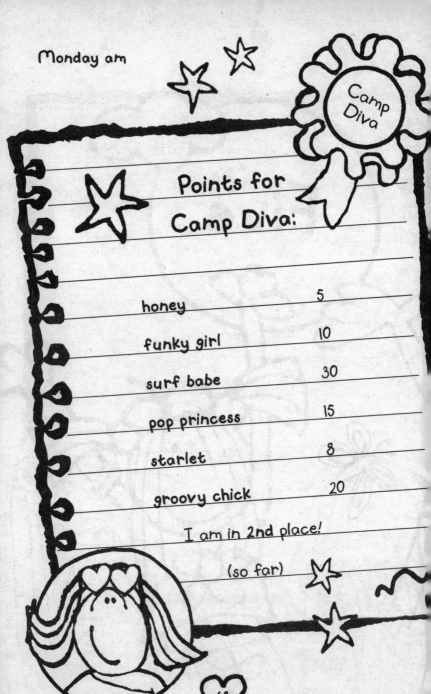

Camp Diva

Points for Camp Diva:

honey	5
funky girl	10
surf babe	30
pop princess	15
starlet	8
groovy chick	20

I am in 2nd place!

(so far)

Starlet was upset because she only

had 8 points!

We made up this song to

cheer her up.

There was starlet.

Let, let.

Feeling all upset.

In the tent,

In the tent!

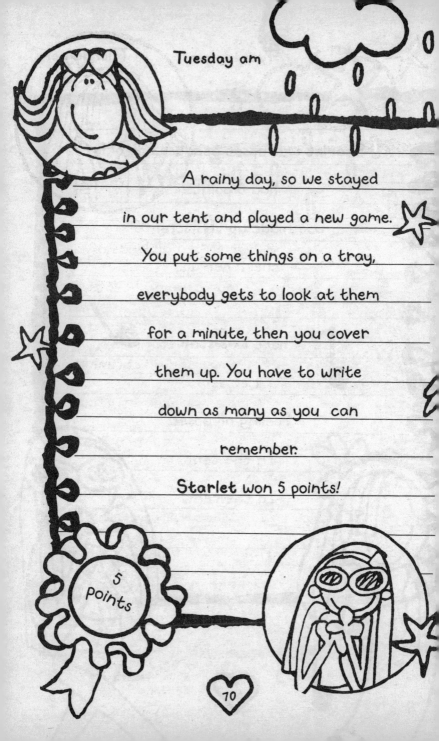

Tuesday am

A rainy day, so we stayed
in our tent and played a new game.
You put some things on a tray,
everybody gets to look at them
for a minute, then you cover
them up. You have to write
down as many as you can
remember.
Starlet won 5 points!

5
points

70

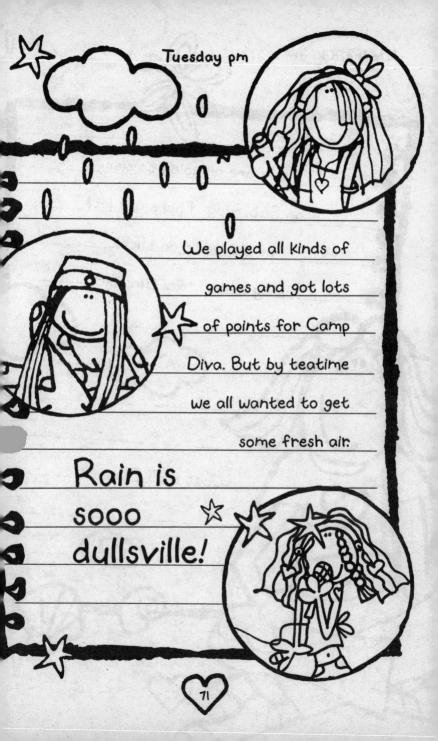

Tuesday pm

We played all kinds of games and got lots of points for Camp Diva. But by teatime we all wanted to get some fresh air.

Rain is sooo dullsville!

71

Wednesday am

We are all going to pier
on Saturday. There are lots
of things to do there,
they have a mini fun fair!

What shall I wear?

Got out my summer skirt and top, but if it gets cold I will freeze. Not very groovy! Maybe jeans and flip-flops will be best.

Thunderstorm!

Pop princess is so scared of thunder.

(Told her so is

my dog).

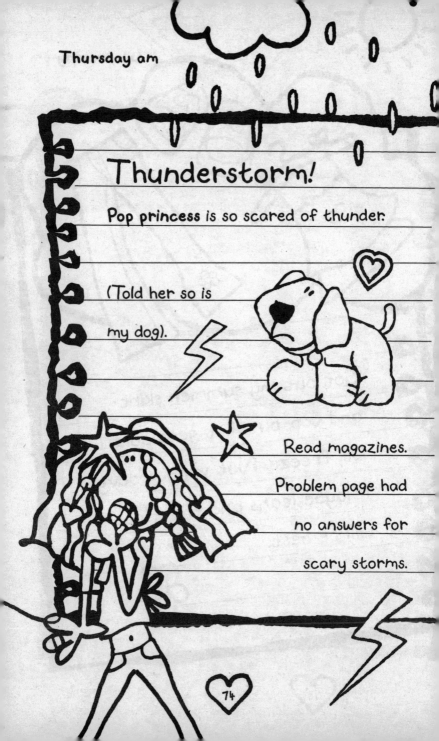

Read magazines.

Problem page had

no answers for

scary storms.

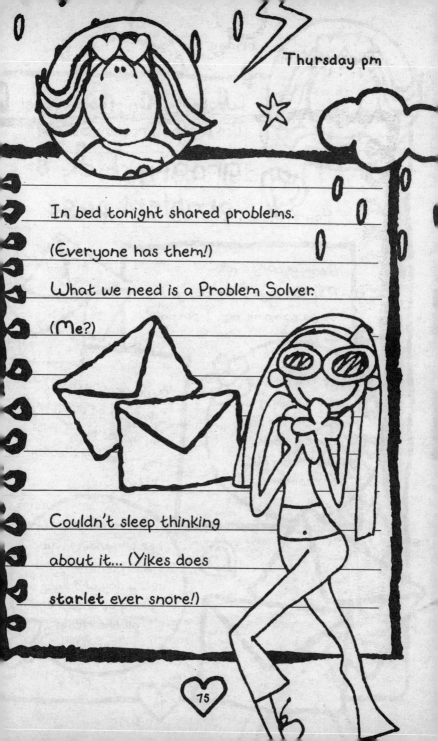

Thursday pm

In bed tonight shared problems.

(Everyone has them!)

What we need is a Problem Solver.

(Me?)

Couldn't sleep thinking

about it... (Yikes does

starlet ever snore!)

Wrote my own problem page!
I'm a good Problem Solver!

groovy chick's problem page

Dear groovy chick,
My dad says I am too young to go camping, but I am not!

Get the adult who is taking you to call. Or how about a back garden camp out for starters?

Dear groovy chick,
I love to go away with my mates but I miss my mum. What can I do?

Try texting her or sending her a postcard. Phone her every day and keep a diary to show her all the things you did!

Got a holiday problem?

Dear groovy chick,
I need to take my cuddly bear with me but I am afraid my mates will laugh at me.

Tell them he's the latest fashion statement. They'll be glad they can get out theirs!

Dear groovy chick,
Can I wear make-up when I am camping?

The golden rule is keep it natural and glam it up for evenings.

Dear groovy chick,
Help! My mate snores!

Roll her onto her side. Wake her. Move to another room or wear pretty pink earplugs.

We love the pier!

We went straight to the fair.
Starlet and I wanted to go on the
dodgems, but everybody else wanted
to go on the big wheel.

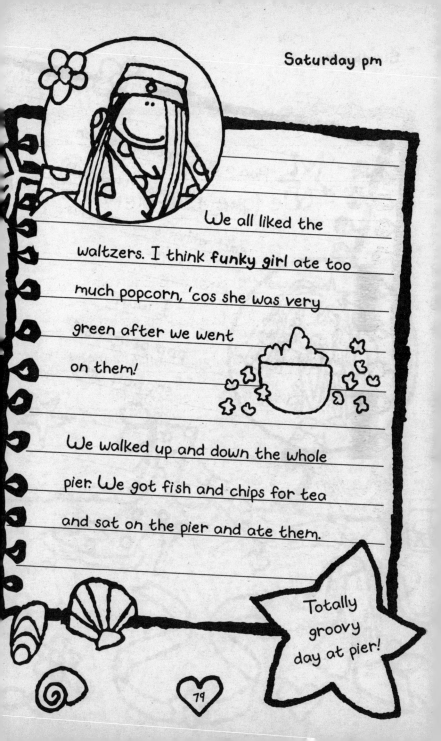

We all liked the waltzers. I think funky girl ate too much popcorn, 'cos she was very green after we went on them!

We walked up and down the whole pier. We got fish and chips for tea and sat on the pier and ate them.

Totally groovy day at pier!

Had a groovy swap session with my mates. Tried out each other's accessories.

I want
pop princess'
spotty bag!

80

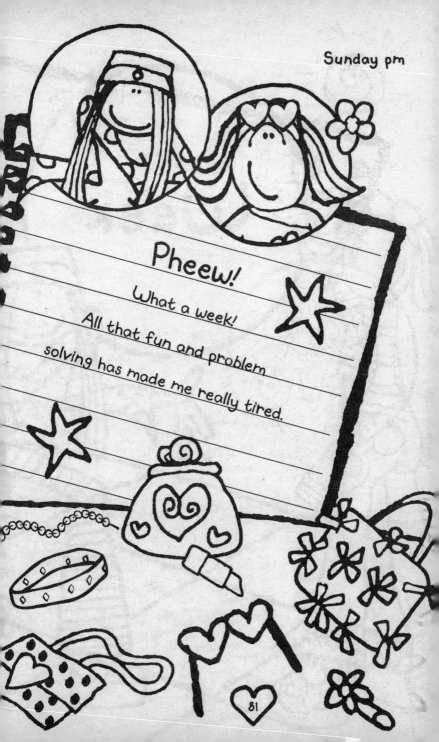

Pheew!

What a week!
All that fun and problem
solving has made me really tired.

81

Week

Six

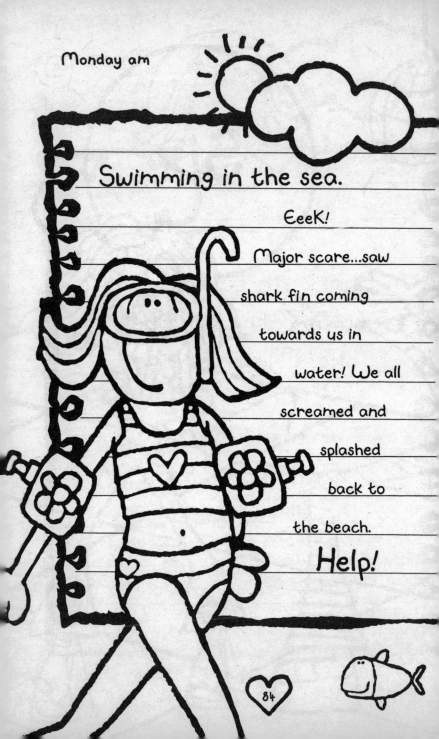

Swimming in the sea.

Eeek!

Major scare...saw

shark fin coming

towards us in

water! We all

screamed and

splashed

back to

the beach.

Help!

84

Shark fin turned out
to be a trick rubber
one! Major cringe!

Boys like that
shouldn't be
allowed out!

Tuesday am

Looking forward to the farewell disco on Wednesday!

We are counting up all the Camp Diva points this morning. I wonder who will win?!

86

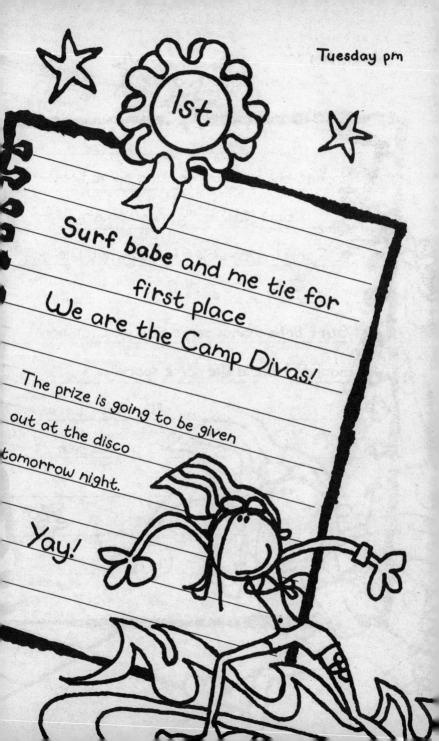

1st

Surf babe and me tie for
first place
We are the Camp Divas!

The prize is going to be given
out at the disco
tomorrow night.

Yay!

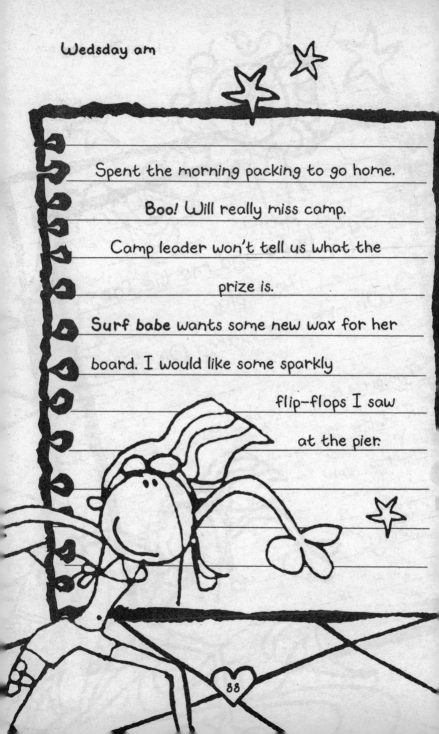

Spent the morning packing to go home.

Boo! Will really miss camp.

Camp leader won't tell us what the

prize is.

Surf babe wants some new wax for her

board. I would like some sparkly

flip-flops I saw

at the pier.

Best night at camp, ever!!

The disco was so groovy.

At the prize giving, surf babe got her wax and I got my flip-flops! And there were shell necklaces that our friends had made!

89

Monday am

My best bits of camp were:

Meeting new people

Camp discos

Making shell necklaces

The beach

The pier

Winning

Camp Diva!

1st

Monday pm

We were all sad on

the bus on the way home.

Sang our camp fire songs to cheer

ourselves up.

Looking forward to seeing

Mum 'n' Dad again.

And the dog.

91

Yay!

Home again!

Unpacked all camp clothes.

Found lots of pictures from

beach and pier.

Mum loved her shell

present.

Am going to wear

new flip-flops and shell

necklace every day to

remind me of camp.

92

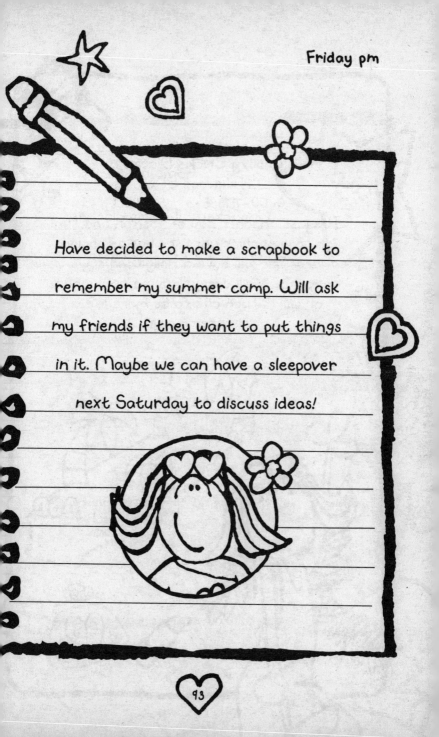

Have decided to make a scrapbook to remember my summer camp. Will ask my friends if they want to put things in it. Maybe we can have a sleepover next Saturday to discuss ideas!

Groovy Chick's Diaries 1:
Hollywood Star
0-00-717636-8   5/4/2004
It's just another day of fashion and fun
for groovy chick until she has a fabulous
idea! She will have a Hollywood style
party. But will everything go as planned
or will it turn out to be more like a
disaster movie?

HOLLYWOOD
X

Groovy Chick's Diaries 3:
Top DJ
0-00-717638-4   6/9/2004
Disco fever gets hold of **groovy chick**
and friends, but being a top DJ is
harder than she realises!
Now you can get into the groove too.
Get ready to disco!

Groovy Chick's Diaries 4:
Circus Crazy
0-00-717641-4   6/9/2004
Swing into action with the one and
only **groovy chick** and friends!
Groovy chick goes circus crazy, but can
she master her big top skills in time
to amaze everyone?

First published in Great Britain by
HarperCollins Children's Books in 2004

1 3 5 7 9 10 8 6 4 2

ISBN: 0 00 717637 6

Bang on the door character copyright:
© 2004 Bang on the Door all rights reserved.
©bang on the door®© is a trademark
Exclusive right to license by Santoro

www.bangonthedoor.com

The HarperCollins website address is:
www.harpercollinschildrensbooks.co.uk